MY NAME IS:

_____

AND I AM MAGICAL

We know how special we are, we know how valuable we are. We know we have tons to offer the world! But sometimes we doubt ourselves, have you ever doubted yourself or felt down about what you had to offer the world?
If so, why did you feel this way and how will you work towards re-affirming all the magic you bring to the world.

Hello Diary

All of us have superpowers. Superpowers are our gifts, talents, and capabilities that make us unique and special. What are your five superpowers?

Not all days are super good days! Some days may not be as good as others. Even on the not so good days, there are tons of things to be grateful for. Write down five things you are grateful for today.

We all desire to be supported by others, for our dreams, ambitions,
and desires to be supported. Do you feel that you have people to support you?
If so, who are those people?

_____

- -

_____

- -

_____

- -

_____

- -

_____

- -

_____

- -

_____

- -

_____

- -

_____

Feelings are very sticky. Sometimes, we feel sad, mad, frustrated, annoyed. But even with these very unpleasant feelings, we can continue in a state of happiness. Do you feel you can talk to people about your feelings? Who are the people you feel most comfortable talking to about your feelings? How do they help you process your feelings and get to a state of resolve?

Do you ever feel alone? Why?

Describe a favorite memory you shared with family.

Having an intention for the day can help our day to be alot better! What is your intention for today? In other words, what do you hope to get out of this day?

_____

- -

_____

- -

_____

- -

_____

- -

_____

- -

_____

- -

_____

- -

_____

What is your favorite sport?

_____

- -

_____

Explain the rules of the game.

_____

- -

_____

- -

_____

- -

_____

- -

_____

- -

_____

Draw a picture of how you are feeling today.

Did you face any challenges today?

What was the high of your day?

_____

- -

_____

_____

- -

_____

_____

- -

_____

What was the low of your day?

_____

- -

_____

_____

- -

_____

_____

- -

_____

All of us have gifts and talents. Gifts and talents are the things that we are good at. What are three gifts and talents of yours?

There are four seasons: Winter, Spring, Summer, Fall.
What is your favorite season and why?

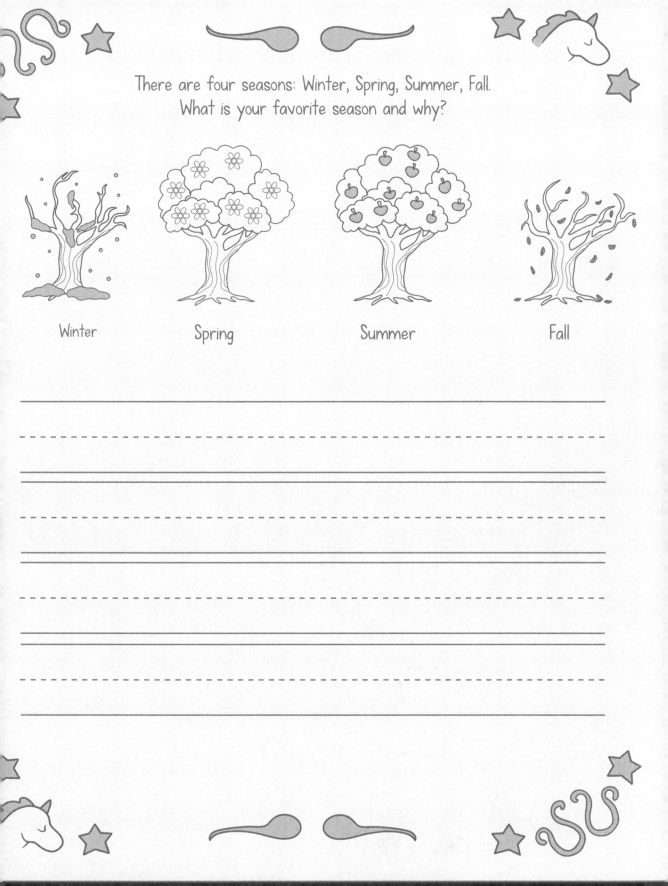

Winter   Spring   Summer   Fall

Describe a favorite memory you shared with friends.

Today's Journal Entry: Write whatever your heart desires,
whatever you are feeling or thinking write here.

If you could use one word to describe your day, what would it be?
Explain why.

_____

- -

_____

- -

_____

- -

_____

- -

_____

- -

_____

- -

_____

Did you feel included today?

What are you most looking forward to tomorrow?

_____

- -

_____

- -

_____

- -

_____

- -

_____

- -

_____

- -

_____

- -

Beaches and candy bring me joy! What brings you joy?

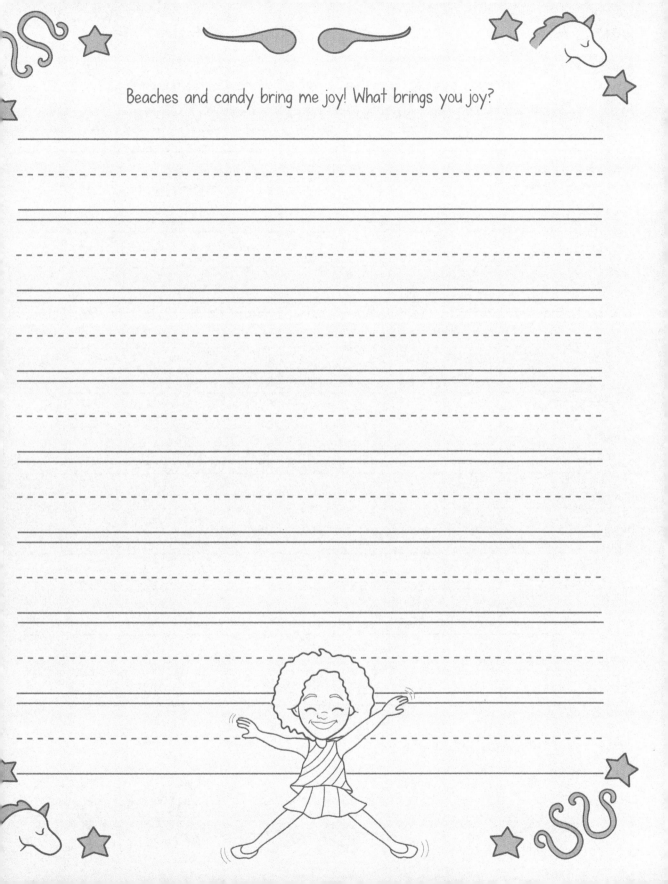

Do you ever get worried? If so, why? How can you work on
"calming your worries", knowing that everything will work out in the best way.

_____

- -

_____

- -

_____

- -

_____

- -

_____

- -

_____

- -

_____

- -

Today's Journal Entry: Write whatever your heart desires,
whatever you are feeling or thinking write here.

Have you ever felt frustrated and allowed your frustrations to overpower you? In order to not allow our frustrations to cause us to do anything we will regret, take a deep breath in and out, and in and out. By breathing, we can begin to relax our bodies. In this moment, think about what is going ok. Be grateful.

Who is your favorite teacher, and why?

If you could have any superpower, what would you have and why?

How do you show someone you love, that you love them?

_____

- -

_____

- -

_____

- -

_____

- -

_____

- -

_____

- -

_____

Today's Journal Entry: Write whatever your heart desires,
whatever you are feeling or thinking write here.

If you could be any animal, what would you be?

Draw here the type of animal you want to be.

I WANT TO BE A: _____

What do you like most about your school environment?

What do you like least about your school environment? What can you do to change this? What can you do to make your school environment better?

How are you feeling today?

What is your favorite color?

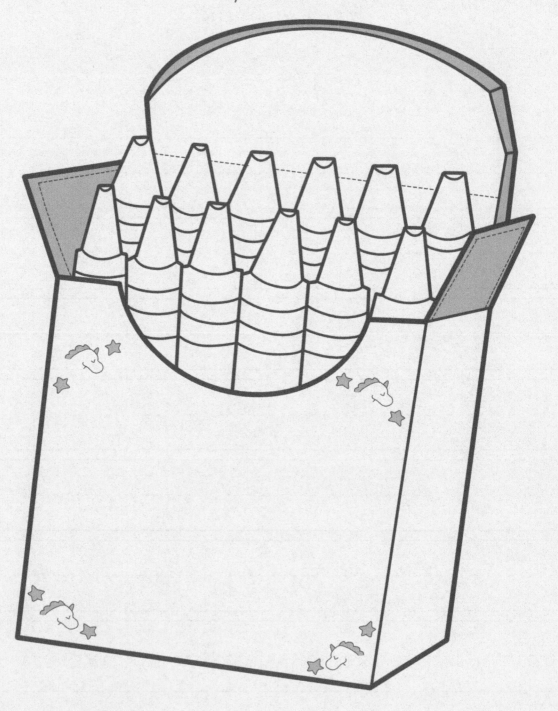

MY FAVORITE COLOR IS: _____

Today's Journal Entry: Write whatever your heart desires, whatever you are feeling or thinking write here.

Have you ever felt afraid? If so, did you allow fear to hold you back?
Why or why not?

"Fear is real, insidious, and damaging. But it can be defeated if we are willing to name it, own it, and use it."

– Stacy Abrams

If you could be any superhero, who would it be and why?

_____

- -

_____

- -

_____

- -

_____

- -

_____

- -

_____

- -

_____

- -

_____

- -

_____

- -

_____

Draw an emoji to represent how you are feeling today.

Put a picture here that shows you incredibly happy!

Today's Journal Entry: Write whatever your heart desires,
whatever you are feeling or thinking write here.

Who do you want to be when you grow up and why?

_____

- -

_____

- -

_____

- -

_____

- -

_____

- -

_____

- -

_____

- -

_____

What is your accomplishment? In other words, what is something you have done or been a part of that you are so very proud of?

_____

- -

_____

- -

_____

- -

_____

- -

_____

- -

_____

- -

_____

- -

_____

How others perceive us is not us. We are how we see ourselves.
How do you see yourself? Who are you?

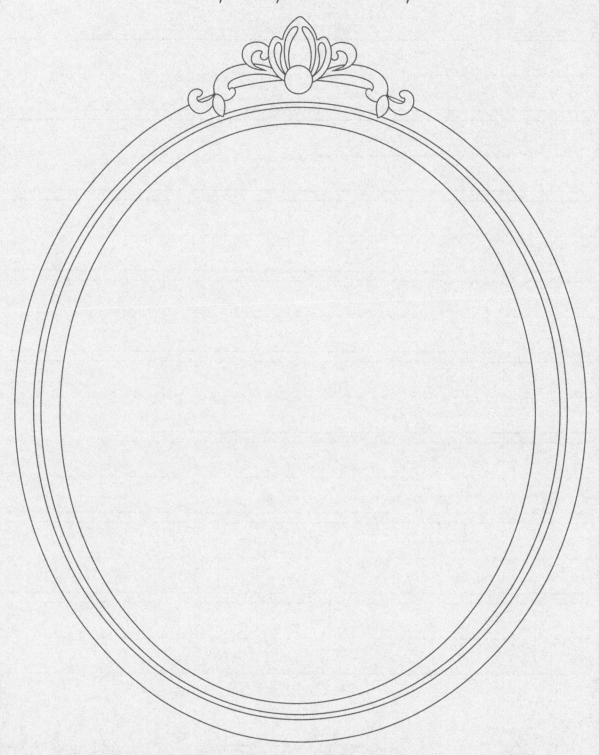

Today's Journal Entry: Write whatever your heart desires,
whatever you are feeling or thinking write here.

Sometimes we fail, we stumble, we face obstacles. But it is not the failure that matters, it is the getting back up that does. How have you overcame any recent failures? What were they and what lessons did you learn?

Write about what feelings you have. For example, do you feel happy, sad, thankful, free? Whatever your feelings, think about them as you feel them and as they pass.

What qualities in your friends do you admire the most?

What are your biggest dreams?

If you had a genie who could give you three wishes, what would your 3 wishes be?

Describe your dream vacation. Where would you go? What would you do?

We know how special we are, we know how valuable we are. We know we have tons to offer the world! But sometimes we doubt ourselves, have you ever doubted yourself or felt down about what you had to offer the world? If so, why did you feel this way and how will you work towards re-affirming all the magic you bring to the world.

All of us have superpowers. Superpowers are our gifts, talents, and capabilities that make us unique and special. What are your five superpowers?

Not all days are super good days! Some days may not be as good as others.
Even on the not so good days, there are tons of things to be grateful for.
Write down five things you are grateful for today.

We all desire to be supported by others, for our dreams, ambitions, and desires to be supported. Do you feel that you have people to support you? If so, who are those people?

_____

- -

_____

- -

_____

- -

_____

- -

_____

- -

_____

- -

_____

- -

Feelings are very sticky. Sometimes, we feel sad, mad, frustrated, annoyed. But even with these very unpleasant feelings, we can continue in a state of happiness. Do you feel you can talk to people about your feelings? Who are the people you feel most comfortable talking to about your feelings? How do they help you process your feelings and get to a state of resolve?

_____

- -

_____

- -

_____

- -

_____

- -

_____

- -

_____

- -

_____

- -

_____

Do you ever feel alone? Why?

_____

- -

_____

- -

_____

- -

_____

- -

_____

- -

_____

- -

_____

- -

_____

- -

_____

Describe a favorite memory you shared with friends.

Today's Journal Entry: Write whatever your heart desires,
whatever you are feeling or thinking write here.

What is your favorite sport?

_____

- -

_____

Explain the rules of the game.

_____

- -

_____

- -

_____

- -

_____

- -

_____

- -

_____

Draw a picture of how you are feeling today.

Did you face any challenges today?

What was the high of your day?

_____

- -

_____

- -

_____

- -

What was the low of your day?

_____

- -

_____

- -

_____

- -

All of us have gifts and talents. Gifts and talents are the things that we are good at.
What are three gifts and talents of yours?

There are four seasons: Winter, Spring, Summer, Fall.
What is your favorite season and why?

Winter   Spring   Summer   Fall

Describe a favorite memory you shared with friends.

Today's Journal Entry: Write whatever your heart desires,
whatever you are feeling or thinking write here.

If you could use one word to describe your day, what would it be?
Explain why.

_____

- -

_____

- -

_____

- -

_____

- -

_____

- -

_____

- -

_____

- -

_____

Did you feel included today?

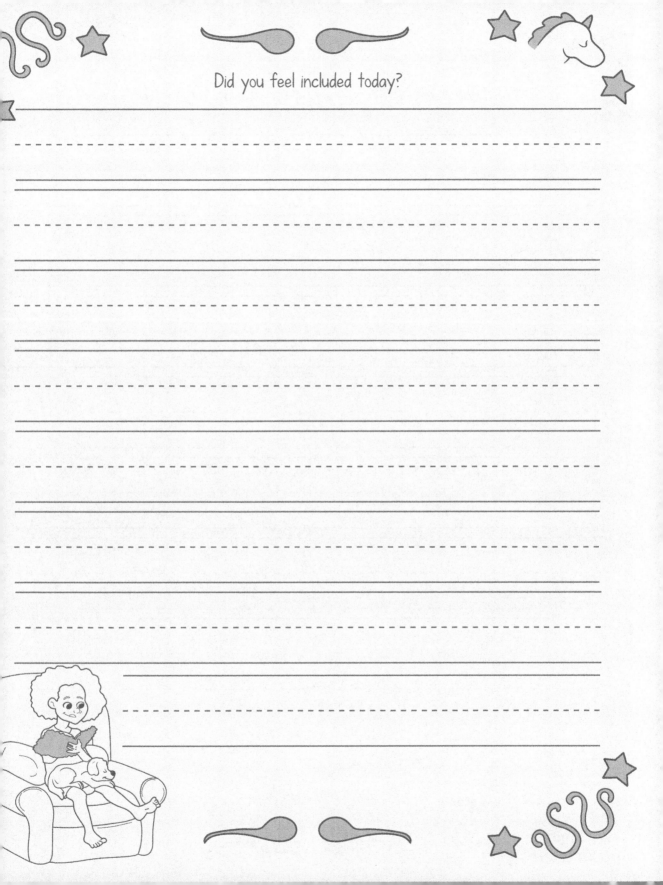

What are you most looking forward to tomorrow?

_____

- -

_____

- -

_____

- -

_____

- -

_____

- -

_____

- -

_____

- -

Beaches and candy bring me joy! What brings you joy?

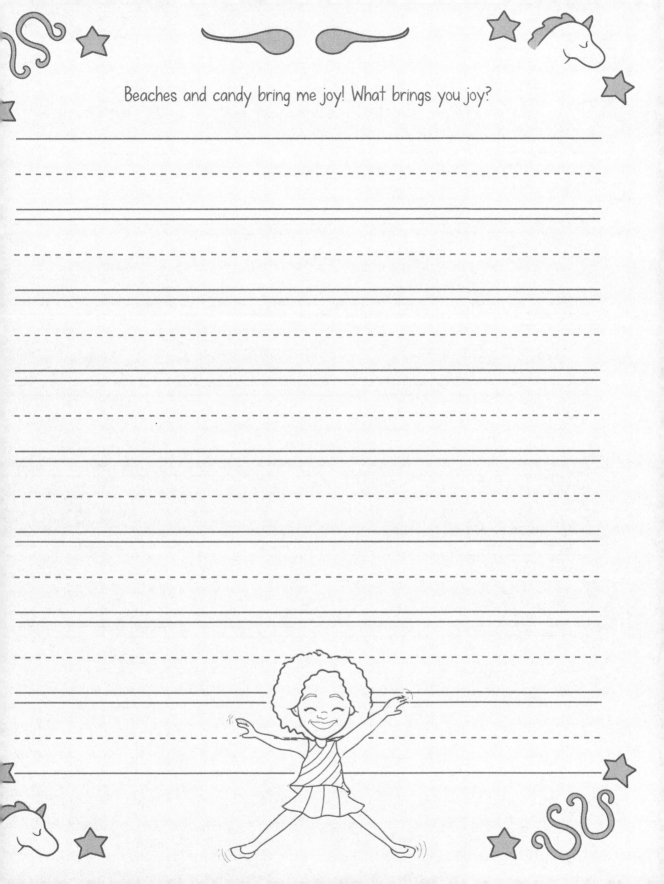

Do you ever get worried? If so, why? How can you work on "calming your worries", knowing that everything will work out in the best way.

_____

- -

_____

- -

_____

- -

_____

- -

_____

- -

_____

- -

_____

Today's Journal Entry: Write whatever your heart desires,
whatever you are feeling or thinking write here.

Have you ever felt frustrated and allowed your frustrations to overpower you? In order to not allow our frustrations to cause us to do anything we will regret, take a deep breath in and out, and in and out. By breathing, we can begin to relax our bodies. In this moment, think about what is going ok. Be grateful.

Who is your favorite teacher, and why?

If you could have any superpower, what would you have and why?

How do you show someone you love, that you love them?

Today's Journal Entry: Write whatever your heart desires, whatever you are feeling or thinking write here.

If you could be any animal, what would you be?

Draw here the type of animal you want to be.

I WANT TO BE A: _____

What do you like most about your school environment?

_____

- -

_____

- -

_____

- -

_____

- -

_____

- -

_____

- -

_____

- -

_____

What do you like least about your school environment? What can you do to change this? What can you do to make your school environment better?

_____

- -

_____

- -

_____

- -

_____

- -

_____

- -

_____

- -

_____

- -

_____

How are you feeling today?

What is your favorite color?

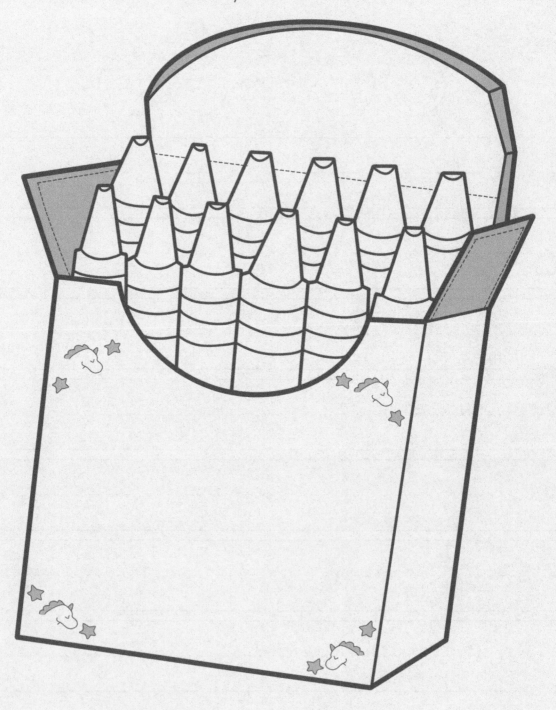

MY FAVORITE COLOR IS: _____

Today's Journal Entry: Write whatever your heart desires, whatever you are feeling or thinking write here.

Have you ever felt afraid? If so, did you allow fear to hold you back?
Why or why not?

_____

- -

_____

- -

_____

- -

_____

- -

_____

- -

_____

- -

_____

- -

_____

> "Fear is real, insidious, and damaging. But it can be defeated if we are willing to name it, own it, and use it."
>
> - Stacy Abrams

If you could be any superhero, who would it be and why?

Draw an emoji to represent how you are feeling today.

Put a picture here that shows you incredibly happy!

Today's Journal Entry: Write whatever your heart desires,
whatever you are feeling or thinking write here.

Who do you want to be when you grow up and why?

_____

- -

_____

- -

_____

- -

_____

- -

_____

- -

_____

- -

_____

- -

_____

What is your greatest accomplishment? In other words, what is something you have done or been a part of that you are so very proud of?

_____

- -

_____

- -

_____

- -

_____

- -

_____

- -

_____

- -

_____

- -

_____

- -

_____

How others perceive us is not us. We are how we see ourselves.
How do you see yourself? Who are you?

Today's Journal Entry: Write whatever your heart desires, whatever you are feeling or thinking write here.

Sometimes we fail, we stumble, we face obstacles. But it is not the failure that matters, it is the getting back up that does. How have you overcame any recent failures? What were they and what lessons did you learn?

Write about what feelings you have. For example, do you feel happy, sad, thankful, free? Whatever your feelings, think about them as you feel them and as they pass.

What qualities in your friends do you admire the most?

What are your biggest dreams?

_____

- -

_____

- -

_____

- -

_____

- -

_____

- -

_____

- -

_____

- -

_____

- -

_____

If you had a genie who could give you three wishes, what would your 3 wishes be?

Describe your dream vacation. Where would you go? What would you do?

Made in the USA
Las Vegas, NV
16 February 2023

67625895R00066